Collins

# Happy Handwriting

## Practice Book 6

The rainforest is a remarkable environment. It accounts for around 30 million species of plants and animals.

The rainforest is a remarkable environment. It accounts for around 30 million species of plants and animals.

Series Editor: Dr Jane Medwell
Author: Stephanie Austwick

William Collins' dream of knowledge for all began with the publication of his first book in 1819. A self-educated mill worker, he not only enriched millions of lives, but also founded a flourishing publishing house. Today, staying true to this spirit, Collins books are packed with inspiration, innovation and practical expertise.

They place you at the centre of a world of possibility and give you exactly what you need to explore it.

Collins. Freedom to teach.

Published by Collins
An imprint of HarperCollins*Publishers*
The News Building, 1 London Bridge Street, London, SE1 9GF, UK

HarperCollins*Publishers*
1st Floor, Watermarque Building, Ringsend Road, Dublin 4, Ireland

Browse the complete Collins catalogue at
**collins.co.uk**

© HarperCollins*Publishers* Limited 2022

10 9 8 7 6 5 4 3 2 1

ISBN 978-0-00-848585-6

British Library Cataloguing-in-Publication Data
A catalogue record for this publication is available from the British Library.

Series Editor: Dr Jane Medwell
Author: Stephanie Austwick
Expert reviewer: Dr Mellissa Prunty
Publisher: Lizzie Catford
Product manager: Sarah Thomas
Project manager: Jayne Jarvis
Development editor: Jane Cotter
Copyeditor: Jilly Hunt
Proofreaders: Claire Throp, Jonathan Perris
Design template and icons: Sarah-Leigh Wills at Happydesigner
Cover designer: Sarah-Leigh Wills at Happydesigner
Illustrations: Jouve India Pvt. Ltd.
Typesetter: Jouve India Pvt. Ltd.
Production controller: Alhady Ali
Printed and bound in the UK using 100% renewable electricity at Martins the Printers Ltd.

MIX
Paper from
responsible sources
FSC™ C007454

This book is produced from independently certified FSC™ paper to ensure responsible forest management. For more information visit: www.harpercollins.co.uk/green

Copy the words as quickly as possible.

quickly                                    tidily

neatly                                     speedily

Copy these words quickly. Then copy them neatly into your book.

practise                                   slowly

Copy this sentence as quickly as you can.

Speed writing can be very useful, but only if you

can still read it.

Copy this passage into your book, using your best handwriting and showing your own style.

Graphology is the study of handwriting.

Graphologists believe that it is possible to learn

a lot about a person from studying their

handwriting.

My very best
handwriting

How does your speed writing compare with your best handwriting?

3

Copy the words.

of off from flew

Copy this sentence, slanting your writing to the right.

The Leaning Tower of Pisa in Italy is known for its dramatic lean to one side.

Copy these words.

frightful fierce

fearful infer

Copy this passage into your book using your best handwriting and showing your own style.

Facts about the Leaning Tower of Pisa

1. The tower is built from white marble.

2. It is eight storeys high with 296 steps.

3. It took 199 years to build.

Have you remembered to form your joins correctly?

Copy the joins.

ri          ra          rm          rt

Copy these jokes into your book, taking extra care with the joins to and from r.

Why is Cinderella so bad at playing football?

She runs away from the ball.

What's the best way to throw a birthday party

on Mars?

You planet.

Copy these words.

weary                    wary

worried                  sorry

Copy this joke into your book, using your best handwriting and showing your own style.

A man walks into a library and says, "I'll have a

cheeseburger and fries, please."

The librarian says, "Sir, you're in a library."

"Sorry," he whispers. "I'll have a cheeseburger

and fries, please."

Look back at your writing. Are the joins to and from r consistent and accurate?

Copy the combinations.

ent          ence          ant          ance

Copy this passage into your book, slanting your writing and taking extra care with the diagonal joins.

The trial of the Big Bad Wolf commenced today. He appeared confident, and some would say a little arrogant, as he strode into court.

Copy these words.

important                    intelligent

brilliant                    evident

Copy this passage into your book, choosing appropriate words to complete it.

brilliance      persistence      intelligence

As the trial continued today, witness Mr W Cutter took the stand. He spoke about the _____ and _____ of the wolf, always sneaking around, trying to steal food. Wolfie is known for his _____ and may still have something up his sleeve.

Are your diagonal joins consistent and correctly spaced?

Copy the words.

all          the          hill          puff

Copy this passage into your book, taking extra care to keep ascenders and descenders parallel.

As you walk through the rainforest, all thoughts

of the outside world vanish. Brightly coloured

butterflies rest on exotic leaves. However, life in

the forest is tough, and survival hangs in the

balance.

Copy the words.

adorable                     tolerable

considerable                 miserable

Copy this passage into your book, using your best handwriting and showing your own style.

The rainforest is a remarkable environment.

It accounts for around 30 million species of

plants and animals. This ecosystem has been stable

for millions of years, but is being destroyed

and some animals will be unable to survive.

Look back at your writing. Are your ascenders and descenders parallel?

Copy the words.

| What | How | When |
|------|-----|------|
| Who | Why | Where |

Copy these exclamations and questions into your book, adding the correct punctuation.

which team is going to win

what a fabulous player she is

why do goalkeepers wear a different kit

where is the nearest athletics track

Copy the words.

| what | how | when |
|------|-----|------|
| who | why | where |

Copy these statements and commands into your book and add capitals and punctuation. Write (statement) or (command) at the end.

do not run onto the pitch when the ball is in play

it can be hard to see who is in the lead

it is a goal when the ball crosses the line

that is why you need to practise

Is your end punctuation correct? Is it accurately placed and spaced?

Copy the words.

neat                    legible

swift                   efficient

Copy the passage as quickly as you can into your book. Make a mark after one minute, then complete the passage.

The bimbledor is an extremely shy creature that is only found in deserted wastelands. It has three glowing eyes, a bulbous nose and fur the colour of blueberries. Its favourite meal is roasted ants.

Evaluation: I can write _____ readable words per minute.

Copy the words.

name                    appearance

habitat                 diet

Set your **one-minute** timer. Copy this passage as quickly as you can into your book. Make a mark after one minute, then complete the passage.

The zoggladon is an extremely fierce creature that is only found in deep, dark forests. It has two glistening eyes, a hideous nose and feathers the colour of gooseberries. Its favourite meal is shrivelled worms.

Evaluation: I can write _____ readable words per minute.

Copy the words.

honoured                    excited

delighted                   sincerely

Copy this formal letter as neatly as you can into your book.

Dear Ms Udechukwu,

Dunkerly School is celebrating its centenary. To

mark the occasion we are inviting you to speak at

our 'Wonderful One Hundred' event on 7th July.

Yours sincerely,

Copy the words.

enjoyed                     excellent

appreciated                 instructive

Copy this formal letter in your best handwriting, showing your own style.

Dear Ms Udechukwu,

I would like to thank you for your recent visit to

Dunkerly School. Your talk was interesting and

informative and you kept us all entertained.

Yours sincerely,

How does your speed writing compare with your best handwriting?

Copy the joins.

er          re          ea          ar

Copy these brief notes as quickly as you can into your book.

- village – lion in street

- lion – Sydney – six years old

- escaped big cat rescue reserve

- early hours – today

Copy the words.

earlier                    magnificent

escaped                    warned

Copy this passage into your book, using your best handwriting and showing your own style.

In the early hours, the emergency services were called to a local village after residents were woken by the roaring of a lion outside their bedroom windows. Sydney, the six-year-old lion, had escaped from a nearby big cat rescue reserve. Residents have been warned to stay indoors.

How does your speed writing of notes compare with your best handwriting? Is it still legible?

Copy this passage into your book as neatly as you can.

*Saskia, who was only four years old, stared at the colourful lights that surrounded her, hardly daring to breathe.*

*"Is this all for me?" she gasped. "I love it!"*

How well do you think you have done in your writing?

My joins to and from r:

Capital letters and end punctuation:

My tall letters:

Set your one-minute timer. Copy this passage into your book as quickly as you can. Make a mark after one minute, then complete the passage.

*Silver paper chains danced overhead, reflecting the glittering scene below. Lights of every colour twinkled in the darkness, like a million stars sparkling in the night sky.*

*Had they really done all this for her? It was magical!*

How well do you think you have done in your writing?

The legibility of my speed writing:

I can write _____ readable words per minute.

Copy the prefixes.

auto

over

micro

out

Complete and copy this sentence.

overcooked   automatic

I set the _____ timer but it didn't work, so

the casserole was very _____.

Copy the words.

necessary

stationery

category

stationary

Copy these instructions in your best handwriting into your book.

Pre-cook the potatoes, onions and corn until soft.

Place in an ovenproof dish.

Pour the tomato sauce over the vegetables.

Cook in a low oven for forty minutes.

Are your horizontal joins accurate and evenly spaced?

Copy the words.

judge                    flying

grudge                   giggling

Copy these safety tips in your best handwriting into your book.

Tips for keeping safe in a lightning storm:

1. Stay inside if possible.

2. Keep away from water and trees.

3. Squat in a ball, but do not lie flat.

Copy the words.

beautiful                unqualified

perfectly                object

Copy this poem in your best handwriting into your book.

The first snowfall

He shuffles silently through the forest,

As the footpath fades in the dusk.

Mysterious figures gather quietly in the gloom,

Wearing the snow-covered garments of winter.

Did you remember to take your pen off the page after completing the descender?

Copy these joins.

iqu          aqu          equ          nqu

Complete this passage, then copy it into your book.

antiques    frequently    unique

I love history, so I _____ visit castles and

other _____ ancient buildings. They are

often full of priceless _____.

Copy these words.

quilt                                    quarter

queue                                    quote

Copy this passage into your book in your best handwriting.

Sudeley Castle has been home to many kings

and queens. Although the living quarters are

private, visitors can marvel at the quality

antiques in the Banqueting Hall and squeeze in

a visit to the quirky Terrace Café for a slice of

homemade quiche.

Remember – you can join to q but not from it!

Copy the contractions.

He'd          It'll          I'll          I've

Complete this diary entry, choosing from the following contractions. You can use each one more than once. Then copy the whole diary entry into your book.

We're     It'll     I'm     I'll     he'll/she'll

Hi Diary,

_____ so excited! _____ going to Gran's today. _____ be great! _____ taking my friend and _____ love it there. _____ tell you all about it tomorrow.

Copy these negative contractions.

doesn't                          weren't

didn't                           isn't

Rewrite this positive diary entry into your book, adding contractions to turn it into a negative one.

Hi Diary,
Gran was very pleased to see us yesterday. She had made us a cake. We were allowed to go to the beach. It was fun.

Are your apostrophes correctly placed and spaced?

Copy the capital letters.

# ABCDEFGHIJKLMNOPQRSTUVWXYZ

Copy this information, taking extra care to ensure capital letters are the correct height.

*Travelling to New York:*

*A direct flight from the UK will take between*

*seven hours and eight hours thirty minutes.*

Copy the words.

| | |
|---|---|
| *Monday* | *Queen* |
| *September* | *Diwali* |

Copy this information into your book using your best handwriting.

*Things to do in New York in March:*

• *Sail around the Statue of Liberty*

• *Walk over the Brooklyn Bridge*

• *March 17th – watch the St Patrick's Day Parade*

Remember – capital letters should be slightly shorter than tall letters, but taller than t.

Copy the conjunctions.

and            but            for

or             so             yet

Copy this online review into your book, taking care with the placing and spacing of the commas.

Super Sports has just opened at the top of the High Street, and it has every item of sport equipment you could wish for. The staff are knowledgeable and helpful, so why not pay them a visit?

Copy the words and punctuation marks.

comma ,            full stop .

semi-colon ;            colon :

Copy these sentences into your book, spacing the semi-colon correctly.

High Town was deserted;everyone was on holiday.

My dad likes coffee;my mum likes tea.

Yesterday we caught the bus;today we walked.

I love the pet shop; my brother loves looking at toys for our cat.

Are your commas and semi-colons accurately placed and spaced?

Copy the words.

time

event

place

directions

Set a timer. Make notes in your book by writing the key information (underlined) as quickly as you can.

How to find the <u>Sky Skateboard Park</u>: From the <u>railway station</u>, go <u>right</u> along <u>Devon Road</u>. At the <u>traffic lights</u>, continue <u>straight ahead</u> until you reach the <u>Shopping Centre</u>. You will see us <u>ahead</u>.

Can you retell the information using just your notes?

Copy the words.

legible

useful

clear

concise

Underline the key information below. Set a timer. Make notes in your book by writing the key information as quickly as you can.

Wear a skateboarding helmet that fits your head snugly. It should have side straps that form a "V" shape around each ear and a buckle that fastens tightly under your chin.

Can you retell the information using just your notes?

Copy the words.

print                    separate

label                    clear

Study the labelling of this map. Copy the labels, printing as neatly as you can.

London

Trafalgar Square

Buckingham Palace

The Houses of Parliament          St Paul's Cathedral

River Thames

The London Eye

Copy the words.

neatness                 clarity

precision                simplicity

Copy this story opening into your book, printing neatly so that it can be read by younger readers.

A long time ago, there was a poor young man called Dick Whittington. He'd heard about a far-away place called London, where everybody was rich and the streets were paved with gold.

It is important to practise printing. When might you use it?

Copy the words.

ape add apple ant

Write the words above in alphabetical order.

In your book, list the following in alphabetical order. Use your best joined handwriting.

Days of the week: Monday, Tuesday, Wednesday, Thursday, Friday, Saturday, Sunday

Months of the year: January, February, March, April, May, June, July, August, September, October, November, December

Copy the words.

alphabetical                              arrange

order                                     title

In your book, rearrange these classic book titles into alphabetical order. As they all begin with 'The' you will need to look at the second word.

The Railway Children; The Secret Garden; The Hobbit; The Jungle Book; The Wind in the Willows; The Iron Man; The Lion, the Witch and the Wardrobe; The Tale of Peter Rabbit.

When and where might you find things arranged in alphabetical order?

Copy this passage into your book as neatly as you can.

# Why do I love daffodils so much?

# They are the messengers of spring.

# Winter has left; summer is on its way.

# Whenever I see daffodils nodding their heads in

# Town Park, I just have to smile.

How well do you think you have done in your writing?

My horizontal joins from o, v, w:

The spacing of semi-colons and commas:

The height of capital letters:

Set a timer. Copy this passage into your book as quickly as you can. Make a mark after one minute, then complete the passage.

# Spring is the season between the colder winter

# months and warmer summer days. Flowers are

# blooming, trees are blossoming and insects, birds

# and animals are preparing to welcome their

# young. It is a season of happiness and hope.

How well do you think you have done in your writing?

The legibility of my speed writing:

I can write _____ readable words per minute.

Copy the words.

wherever                    nevertheless

however                     whatever

Make ten compound words using the words below and write them into your book.

| air | day | dream | field | time | way |
|-----|-----|-------|-------|------|-----|
| bed | clothes | break | port | room | light |

Copy the words.

sunglasses                  bathroom

shopkeeper                  thunderstorm

Choose the hyphenated compound word that matches each example. Note the spacing of the hyphen. Copy the examples and compound words neatly into your book.

man-eating          well-written
accident-prone      baby-faced

A person who looks young _____

A dangerous crocodile _____

An extremely good novel _____

Someone who falls over often _____

Are your hyphenated compound words correctly spaced? Think of three more examples.

Copy the words.

style                    glide

slope                    appearance

Copy the handwritten note into your book, slanting your writing to the right.

Dear committee member,

It's that time of year again! We need to

start thinking about the Summer Fair.

I'm holding a meeting at my house

next Tuesday, at 7 o'clock.

Refreshments provided. I hope you

can make it.

Copy the words.

similar                  like

same                     close

Copy this agenda into your book in your best handwriting.

## Summer Fair – Agenda

1.  Introductions and welcome to any newcomers.

2.  Review of last year. What went well?

3.  Ideas for this year?

Did you remember to slant your writing to the right?

Copy the words.

actually                    decode

enquired                    dancing

Complete the sentences using the words below, then copy the sentences into your book.

| acquiring   acquisition   acquire   acquired |

1. My tennis club needs to _____

   some new players.

2. We _____ a few last year.

3. We are always _____ new players.

4. Adeel has been a good _____.

Copy the words.

weather                    underground

principle                    damaged

Copy this blog into your book in your best joined handwriting.

The annual tournament took place on Saturday

between Regal Tennis Club and The Togas.

Unfortunately, the weather was against us,

and play had to be abandoned.

Look back at your joins to and from round letters. Are they even and accurate?

Copy the words.

right                                    fright

after                                    retell

Complete this passage, then copy it into your book.

| transfer | reverse | prefer | differ | prefers |

In the future, we will have to _____ to a

new school. I _____ one school. Once you

have decided, you can't _____ your decision.

Copy the words.

friend                                   review

recommend                                forefront

Copy this advertisement into your book in your best handwriting.

Fairfield School – friendships for life.
• Caring and professional staff.
• A broad range of subjects on offer.
• Recently refurbished sport facilities.
For further information, please contact
the office.

Did you remember to write words with f and r correctly?

Copy the words.

correct                  amend

improve                  change

Proofread this handwritten letter extract, correct it and then rewrite it neatly into your book.

Yesturday, i wnet to the beech and
i was disgusting at the ammount of
litter. Theire was plastic bottles food
rappers and even brocken toys. dont
people realise that all this rubish
gets washed of the beech and into th ocean

Copy the words.

idea                     sense

theme                    paragraph

Copy the information as two paragraphs into your book in your neatest handwriting.

Plastic is an amazing material with many uses.

Unfortunately, plastic waste harms life in our

oceans. Many sea turtles have eaten plastic

rubbish.

How do paragraphs help us with comprehension?

Copy the words.

commas

brackets

dashes

parenthesis

Underline the additional information in each sentence. Rewrite this passage into your book, placing and spacing the commas for parenthesis.

A strange creature which had appeared out of nowhere blocked their path. Sofia the bravest in the group stepped forward.

Copy the words.

informal

extra

idea

information

Copy this paragraph into your book, spacing the punctuation correctly.

Its features—one eye,green hair and a large red mouth—gave it a comical look. Sofia,who was not feeling very brave,smiled at the creature. The large red mouth—the creature's,not Sofia's—began to curve upwards. It was smiling.

How do commas and dashes help to clarify meaning or add interest?

Copy the words.

Stop!                                   Check!

Wait!                                   Move!

Set a timer. Copy the instructions into your book quickly, making a mark after one minute.

Stay safe this summer – the sea:

1. Don't swim in the sea without an adult.

2. Always swim between the flags.

3. Don't swim in very cold water for too long.

4. Don't use inflatables unsupervised.

Evaluation: I can write _____ readable words per minute.

Copy the words.

efficiency                              fluency

Set a timer. Copy the instructions into your book quickly, making a mark after one minute.

Stay safe this summer – rivers and canals:

1. SAFE – Stay Away From the Edge.

2. Never swim alone in deep water.

3. Beware of hidden hazards – rocks and rubbish.

Evaluation: I can write _____ readable words per minute.

Is your quick writing legible? Can you remember the instructions?

Copy the words.

precise          careful

thorough          formal

Copy this handwritten school report in your neatest handwriting into your book.

> Sam has shown great improvement this term. She has worked particularly hard on her handwriting, which is now neat, fluent and legible. She is practising slanting her writing and making correct joins.

Copy the words.

**personal**          **practising**

**practise**          **practice**

Class 6L has written a report for their teacher. Copy this in your neatest handwriting into your book.

> Mr Nguyen has worked extremely hard on his handwriting this year. His modelling on the board is now fluent and legible, and his written comments in books have shown great improvement.

How does your neat writing compare with your quick writing?

Copy the words.

punctuation

capital letters

Proofread this paragraph and rewrite it correctly into your book.

Summer is the hottest season on the year. the temperature can stay warm and the day are longer. in the uk summer is regarded as june july and august but in australia is is december january and february

Copy the words.

improvement                    editing

construction                   effect

Edit and improve this passage. Write it neatly into your book.

In the summer holidays, it is nice to do something different. Some people like to go for walks. Some people like to go to the park. Some people like to go on holiday. It is nice to be able to relax and enjoy the nicer weather.

Did you remember to slant your writing to the right?

Copy this passage as neatly as you can into your book.

My name is Francisco, or Fran for short, and

I have spent all of my life living in a small village.

Next week, my family is moving to the city.

I am excited, of course, but also a little scared.

How well do you think you have done in your writing?

Formation and spacing of tricky joins:

Placing and spacing of commas for parenthesis:

Height of capital letters:

Set a timer. Copy this passage into your book as quickly as you can. Make a mark after one minute, then complete the passage.

I remember my first evening at summer camp

as if it was yesterday.

We went to the dining room to eat, and everyone

seemed to have a friend, but I was alone.

"Come and sit here," chirruped a voice, and a

life-long friendship was born.

How well do you think you have done in your writing?

The legibility of my speed writing:

I can write _____ readable words per minute.